Intermediate 2 | Units 1, 2 & Applications

Mathematics

Leckie×Leckie

First exam published in 2002.

Published by Leckie & Leckie Ltd, 3rd Floor, 4 Queen Street, Edinburgh EH2 1JE

tel: 0131 220 6831 fax: 0131 225 9987 enquiries@leckieandleckie.co.uk www.leckieandleckie.co.uk

ISBN 1-84372-430-8   ISBN-13 978-1-84372-430-8

A CIP Catalogue record for this book is available from the British Library.

Printed in Scotland by Scotprint.

Leckie & Leckie is a division of Granada Learning Limited.

Leckie & Leckie is grateful to the copyright holders, as credited at the back of the book, for permission to use their material. Every effort has been made to trace the copyright holders and to obtain their permission for the use of copyright material. Leckie & Leckie will gladly receive information enabling them to rectify any error or omission in subsequent editions.

2002 | Intermediate 2 Winter Diet

[BLANK PAGE]

W101/202

NATIONAL
QUALIFICATIONS
2002

FRIDAY, 18 JANUARY
9.00 AM – 9.45 AM

MATHEMATICS
INTERMEDIATE 2
Units 1, 2 and
Applications of Mathematics
Paper 1
(Non-calculator)

Read carefully

1 **You may NOT use a calculator.**

2 Full credit will be given only where the solution contains appropriate working.

3 Square-ruled paper is provided.

SCOTTISH
QUALIFICATIONS
AUTHORITY

FORMULAE LIST

Sine rule: $\dfrac{a}{\sin A} = \dfrac{b}{\sin B} = \dfrac{c}{\sin C}$

Cosine rule: $a^2 = b^2 + c^2 - 2bc \cos A$ or $\cos A = \dfrac{b^2 + c^2 - a^2}{2bc}$

Area of a triangle: $\text{Area} = \dfrac{1}{2}ab \sin C$

Volume of a sphere: $\text{Volume} = \dfrac{4}{3}\pi r^3$

Volume of a cone: $\text{Volume} = \dfrac{1}{3}\pi r^2 h$

Volume of a cylinder: $\text{Volume} = \pi r^2 h$

Standard deviation: $s = \sqrt{\dfrac{\sum(x - \bar{x})^2}{n-1}} = \sqrt{\dfrac{\sum x^2 - (\sum x)^2 / n}{n-1}}$, where n is the sample size.

ALL questions should be attempted.

Marks

1. The marks of a group of students in a class test and in the final exam are shown in the scattergraph below.

   A line of best fit has been drawn.

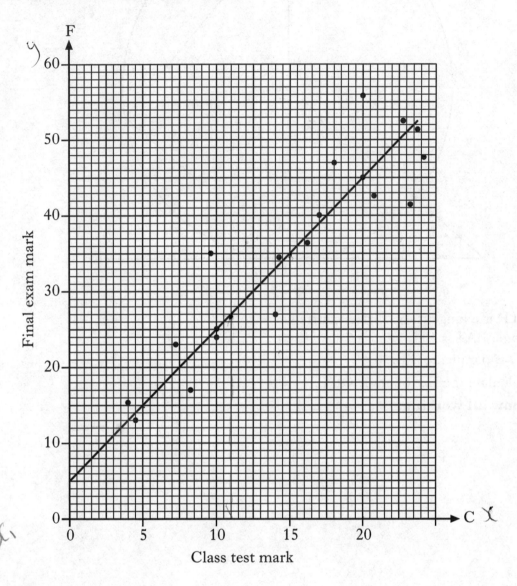

Class test mark

(a) Find the equation of the line of best fit.   **3**

(b) **Use your answer to part (a)** to predict the final exam mark for a student who achieved a mark of 12 in the class test.   **1**

[Turn over

Marks

2.

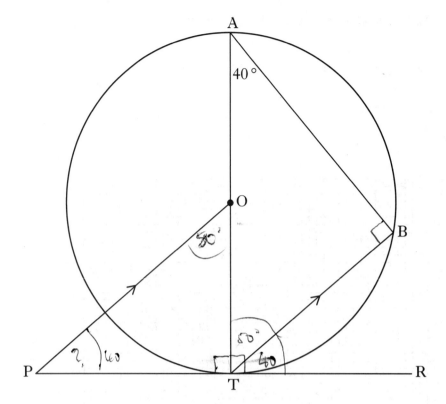

PTR is a tangent to a circle, centre O.

Angle BAT = 40°.

PO is parallel to TB.

Calculate the size of angle OPT.

Show all working.

3

Marks

3. The stem and leaf diagram shows the heights, to the nearest centimetre, of a group of female students.

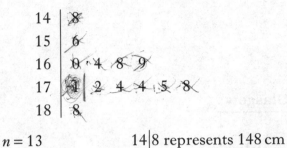

14	8
15	6
16	0 4 8 9
17	1 2 4 4 5 8
18	8

$n = 13$　　　　　　14|8 represents 148 cm

(a) Using the above information, find

  (i) the median　　　　　　　　　　　　　　　　　　　　　　　1

  (ii) the lower quartile and the upper quartile.　　　　　　　　　2

(b) Draw a boxplot to illustrate this data.　　　　　　　　　　　　　2

(c) A sample of male students from the same course was taken. The heights, to the nearest centimetre, of these students were recorded.

The boxplot, shown below, illustrates this new data.

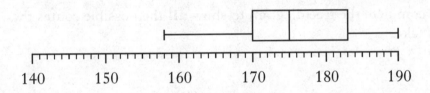

140　　　150　　　160　　　170　　　180　　　190

By comparing the boxplots, make **two** appropriate comments about the heights of the female and the male students.　　　　　　　　　　　　2

[Turn over

Marks

4. The mileage chart shown below indicates how far it is between four places in Scotland.

Inverness

174	
Glasgow	
65	102	**Fort William**
106	149	157	**Aberdeen**

A lorry driver leaves Inverness and has to make deliveries to Glasgow, Fort William and Aberdeen. He cannot go through any place more than once and does not need to return to Inverness.

(a) Copy and complete the tree diagram to show **all** the possible routes the driver can take.

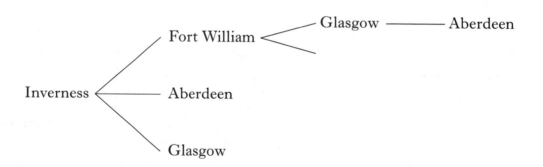

3

(b) He decides to take the route

Inverness — Fort William — Glasgow — Aberdeen.

What distance is this route?

1

Marks

5. The distance, S metres, travelled by an accelerating object is given by the formula

$$S = ut + \tfrac{1}{2}at^2$$

where u metres per second is the initial velocity,

t seconds is the time taken

and a metres per second per second is the acceleration.

(a) Calculate S when $u = 30$, $t = 5$ and $a = 4$. **3**

(b) Calculate u when $S = 294$, $t = 6$ and $a = 3$. **3**

6.

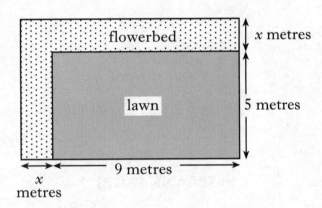

The diagram shows a rectangular garden which consists of a rectangular lawn and a flowerbed along two sides of the lawn

- the lawn measures 9 metres by 5 metres
- the width of the flowerbed is x metres.

(a) State the length and breadth of the garden. **1**

(b) Show that the area, A square metres, of the garden is given by

$$A = x^2 + 14x + 45.$$ **2**

[END OF QUESTION PAPER]

[BLANK PAGE]

W101/204

NATIONAL QUALIFICATIONS 2002	FRIDAY, 18 JANUARY 10.05 AM – 11.35 AM	MATHEMATICS INTERMEDIATE 2 Units 1, 2 and Applications of Mathematics Paper 2

Read carefully

1 **Calculators may be used in this paper.**

2 Full credit will be given only where the solution contains appropriate working.

3 Square-ruled paper is provided.

SCOTTISH
QUALIFICATIONS
AUTHORITY

FORMULAE LIST

Sine rule:
$$\frac{a}{\sin A} = \frac{b}{\sin B} = \frac{c}{\sin C}$$

Cosine rule:
$$a^2 = b^2 + c^2 - 2bc \cos A \text{ or } \cos A = \frac{b^2 + c^2 - a^2}{2bc}$$

Area of a triangle:
$$\text{Area} = \frac{1}{2}ab \sin C$$

Volume of a sphere:
$$\text{Volume} = \frac{4}{3}\pi r^3$$

Volume of a cone:
$$\text{Volume} = \frac{1}{3}\pi r^2 h$$

Volume of a cylinder:
$$\text{Volume} = \pi r^2 h$$

Standard deviation:
$$s = \sqrt{\frac{\sum(x - \bar{x})^2}{n-1}} = \sqrt{\frac{\sum x^2 - (\sum x)^2 / n}{n-1}}, \text{ where } n \text{ is the sample size.}$$

ALL questions should be attempted.

Marks

1. Mary McIntosh works in a knitwear factory.

   For a basic 35-hour week she is paid at the rate of £5·20 per hour and for each jumper she makes over her target of 150, she receives a bonus of £1·35.

   Calculate her gross pay for a week when she makes 200 jumpers.

   3

2. In the diagram opposite AC and BD are arcs of circles with centres at O.

   The radius, OA, is 8 metres and the radius, OB, is 10 metres.

   Angle AOC = 72°.

   Find the shaded area.

   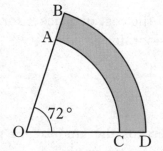

   4

3. The value of a house increased from £85 000 to £86 700 in one year.

   (a) What was the percentage increase?

   1

   (b) If the value of the house continued to rise at this rate, what would its value be after a **further** 3 years?

   Give your answer to the nearest thousand pounds.

   3

4. A grain store is in the shape of a cylinder with a hemisphere on top as shown in the diagram.

   The cylinder has radius 2·4 metres and height 9·5 metres.

   Find the volume of the grain store.

   Give your answer in cubic metres, correct to 1 significant figure.

   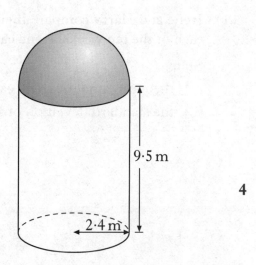

   4

[Turn over

Marks

5. At an amusement park, the Green family buy 3 tickets for the ghost train and 2 tickets for the sky ride. The total cost is £8·60.

   (*a*) Let *x* pounds be the cost of a ticket for the ghost train and *y* pounds be the cost of a ticket for the sky ride.

      Write down an equation in *x* and *y* which satisfies the above condition.   **1**

   (*b*) The Black family bought 5 tickets for the ghost train and 3 tickets for the sky ride at the same amusement park. The total cost was £13·60.

      Write down a second equation in *x* and *y* which satisfies this condition.   **1**

   (*c*) Find the cost of a ticket for the ghost train and the cost of a ticket for the sky ride.   **4**

6. Harry records the amount, in pounds, he earned from his part-time job each week for ten weeks.

$$14 \quad 18 \quad 19 \quad 20 \quad 17 \quad 19 \quad 18 \quad 20 \quad 15 \quad 22$$

He calculates that

$$\sum x = 182 \qquad \text{and} \qquad \sum x^2 = 3364$$

where *x* is the amount in pounds he earned each week.

   (*a*) Calculate the mean amount he earned per week.   **1**

   (*b*) Using an appropriate formula, calculate the standard deviation.   **2**

   (*c*) Irene and Harry compare their earnings over the ten week period. For each of the ten weeks, Irene earns exactly £5 more than Harry.

      State:

      (i) the mean amount Irene earned per week;   **1**

      (ii) the standard deviation of Irene's earnings.   **1**

Marks

7. A field with sides measuring 12·5 metres, 13·2 metres and 10·7 metres is represented by the triangle PQR shown below.

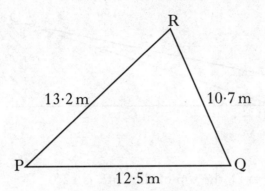

(a) Calculate the size of angle PQR.
   Do not use a scale drawing.

3

(b) Calculate the area of the field.

2

8. A network is **traversable** if it can be drawn by going over every line once and only once without lifting your pencil.

The network shown opposite
can be traversed by the route:

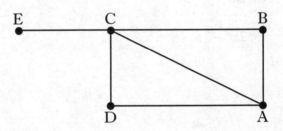

$A \rightarrow C \rightarrow B \rightarrow A \rightarrow D \rightarrow C \rightarrow E$

(a) Write down a route by which the network below can be traversed.

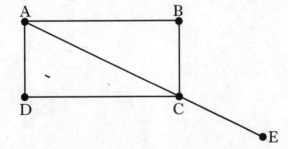

1

(b) Write down a route by which the network below can be traversed.

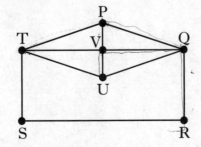

1

Marks

9. To calculate the height of a cliff, a surveyor measures the angle of elevation at two positions A and B as shown in the diagram below.

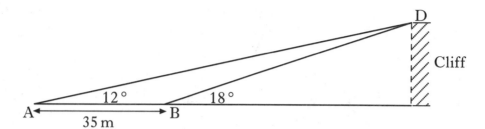

At A, the angle of elevation to D, the top of the cliff, is 12°.

At B, the angle of elevation to D is 18°.

AB is 35 metres.

Calculate the height of the cliff. **5**

10. (*a*) Multiply out the brackets and collect like terms.

$$(2x + 3)(x^2 - 5x + 2)$$ **3**

(*b*) Factorise

$$2x^2 - 7x - 9.$$ **2**

Marks

11. On a spreadsheet, Margaret keeps track of her electricity account for which she receives a statement every two months. She makes a monthly payment towards the cost of the electricity used.

	A	B	C	D	E	F	G
1	**Electricity Account**						
2							
3							
4							
5	**Statements**	**2001**					
6							
7	January–February	£134.68			Monthly payment for 2001	£43.50	
8	March–April	£110.92					
9	May–June	£78.30					
10	July–August	£50.65			**Total paid 2001**		
11	September–October	£64.81					
12	November–December	£104.24					
13							
14	**Total cost for 2001**						
15							
16					**Amount owing**		
17							
18							
19							
20					**Monthly payment for 2002**		
21							
22							

(a) Write down the **formula** for cell B14 to calculate her total annual cost for 2001. 　　1

(b) Margaret chooses to pay £43·50 per month towards the cost of her electricity.

Write down the **formula** for cell F10. 　　1

(c) In cell F16, the formula is

B14–F10.

Calculate the **amount** that will appear in this cell. 　　1

(d) Margaret estimates that her total payment for the year 2002 will be her total cost for 2001 plus 10%.

For cell F20, write down the **formula** for her estimated monthly payment for 2002. 　　2

[Turn over

Marks

12. An article in a Sunday magazine was analysed to provide a measure of the reading difficulty factor. The number of words in each of the first thirty sentences was recorded.

$$
\begin{array}{cccccccccc}
21 & 22 & 28 & 20 & 17 & 8 & 24 & 17 & 17 & 22 \\
5 & 21 & 10 & 17 & 25 & 24 & 14 & 36 & 10 & 34 \\
28 & 6 & 23 & 31 & 39 & 9 & 8 & 15 & 6 & 14
\end{array}
$$

(a) Construct a frequency table with class intervals

      1–5,   6–10,   11–15 etc.   **2**

(b) Calculate the mean number of words per sentence.   **4**

[END OF QUESTION PAPER]

[BLANK PAGE]

X101/202

NATIONAL QUALIFICATIONS 2003	WEDNESDAY, 21 MAY 1.30 PM – 2.15 PM	MATHEMATICS INTERMEDIATE 2 Units 1, 2 and Applications of Mathematics Paper 1 (Non-calculator)

Read carefully

1 **You may <u>NOT</u> use a calculator.**

2 Full credit will be given only where the solution contains appropriate working.

3 Square-ruled paper is provided.

FORMULAE LIST

Sine rule: $\dfrac{a}{\sin A} = \dfrac{b}{\sin B} = \dfrac{c}{\sin C}$

Cosine rule: $a^2 = b^2 + c^2 - 2bc \cos A$ or $\cos A = \dfrac{b^2 + c^2 - a^2}{2bc}$

Area of a triangle: $\text{Area} = \frac{1}{2}ab \sin C$

Volume of a sphere: $\text{Volume} = \frac{4}{3}\pi r^3$

Volume of a cone: $\text{Volume} = \frac{1}{3}\pi r^2 h$

Volume of a cylinder: $\text{Volume} = \pi r^2 h$

Standard deviation: $s = \sqrt{\dfrac{\sum(x - \bar{x})^2}{n-1}} = \sqrt{\dfrac{\sum x^2 - (\sum x)^2 / n}{n-1}}$, where n is the sample size.

ALL questions should be attempted.

Marks

1. Joseph works as a childminder.

   He is paid at a rate of £4·10 per hour for weekdays and at time and a half for weekends.

   One week he works from 9 am till 1pm every day except Sunday.

   Calculate Joseph's gross pay for that week.

   3

2. Two spinners are used in an experiment.

   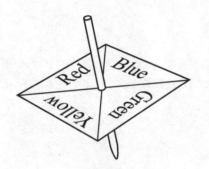 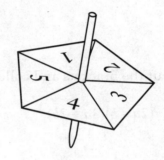

   The table below shows some of the possible outcomes when both spinners are spun and allowed to come to rest.

	1	2	3	4	5
Red	R,1	R,2	R,3	R,4	R,5
Yellow	Y,1	Y,2	Y,3	Y,4	Y,5
Blue	B,1	B,2	B,3	B,4	B,5
Green	G,1	G,2	G,3	G,4	G,5

   (a) Copy and complete the table.

   1

   (b) What is the probability that one spinner comes to rest on red and the other on an even number?

   1

   [Turn over

Marks

3. The diagram shows a cone.

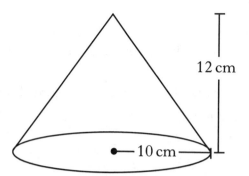

12 cm

10 cm

The height is 12 centimetres and the radius of the base 10 centimetres.
Calculate the volume of the cone.
Take $\pi = 3 \cdot 14$.

2

4. (*a*) Multiply out the brackets and collect like terms.

$$(2a - b)(3a + 2b)$$

2

(*b*) Factorise $7 + 6x - x^2$.

2

Marks

5. A hotel books taxis from a company called QUICKCARS.

The receptionist notes the waiting time for every taxi ordered over a period of two weeks.

The times are recorded in the stem and leaf diagram shown below.

Waiting time (minutes)

```
0 | 6  7
1 | 2  3  4
2 | 5  6  9  9
3 | 2  5  7
4 | 2  4
```

n = 14   1 | 3 represents 13 minutes

(a) For the given data, calculate:

   (i)   the median;   1

   (ii) the lower quartile;   1

   (iii) the upper quartile.   1

(b) Calculate the semi-interquartile range.   1

In another two week period, the hotel books taxis from a company called FASTCABS.

The semi-interquartile range for FASTCABS is found to be 2·5 minutes.

(c) Which company provides the more consistent service?

Give a reason for your answer.   1

6. The diagram below shows part of the London Underground railway network.

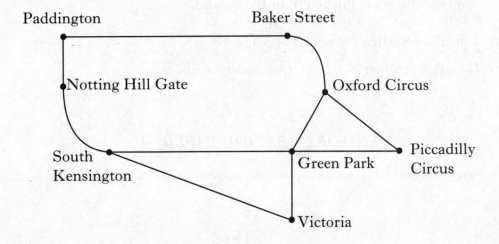

An inspector has to travel along every route shown.

Is it possible to do this without travelling any route more than once?

Explain your answer.   2

[Turn over for Questions 7 and 8 on *Page six*

Marks

7.

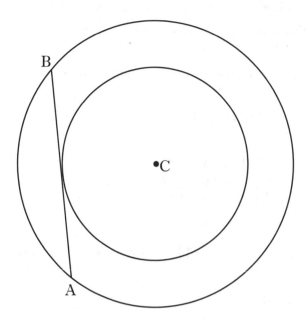

C is the centre of two concentric circles.

AB is a tangent to the smaller circle and a chord of the larger circle.

The radius of the smaller circle is 6 centimetres and the chord AB has length 16 centimetres.

Calculate the radius of the larger circle.

3

8. The surface area, S square centimetres, of a cuboid is given by the formula

$$S = 2lb + 2bh + 2lh$$

where l centimetres is the length of the cuboid
b centimetres is the breadth of the cuboid
h centimetres is the height of the cuboid.

(a) Calculate S when $l = 8\cdot5$, $b = 4\cdot5$ and $h = 5\cdot5$.

2

(b) Calculate h when $S = 2170$, $l = 30$ and $b = 20$.

3

[END OF QUESTION PAPER]

X101/204

| NATIONAL QUALIFICATIONS 2003 | WEDNESDAY, 21 MAY 2.35 PM – 4.05 PM | MATHEMATICS INTERMEDIATE 2 Units 1, 2 and Applications of Mathematics Paper 2 |

Read carefully

1 **Calculators may be used in this paper.**

2 Full credit will be given only where the solution contains appropriate working.

3 Square-ruled paper is provided.

FORMULAE LIST

Sine rule: $\dfrac{a}{\sin A} = \dfrac{b}{\sin B} = \dfrac{c}{\sin C}$

Cosine rule: $a^2 = b^2 + c^2 - 2bc \cos A$ or $\cos A = \dfrac{b^2 + c^2 - a^2}{2bc}$

Area of a triangle: $\text{Area} = \frac{1}{2}ab \sin C$

Volume of a sphere: $\text{Volume} = \frac{4}{3}\pi r^3$

Volume of a cone: $\text{Volume} = \frac{1}{3}\pi r^2 h$

Volume of a cylinder: $\text{Volume} = \pi r^2 h$

Standard deviation: $s = \sqrt{\dfrac{\sum(x - \bar{x})^2}{n-1}} = \sqrt{\dfrac{\sum x^2 - (\sum x)^2 / n}{n-1}}$, where n is the sample size.

ALL questions should be attempted.

Marks

1.

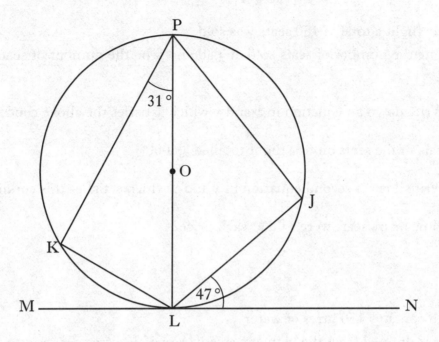

The tangent, MN, touches the circle, centre O, at L.

Angle JLN = 47°.

Angle KPL = 31°.

Find the size of angle KLJ.

3

2. A sample of shoppers was asked which brand of washing powder they preferred.

The responses are shown below.

Washing Powder	Frequency
Dazzle	250
Cyclo	375
Surfer	125
Cleano	250

Construct a pie chart to illustrate this information.

Show all your working.

3

[Turn over

Marks

3. Seats on flights from London to Edinburgh are sold at two prices, £30 and £50.

   On one flight a total of 130 seats was sold.

   Let x be the number of seats sold at £30 and y be the number of seats sold at £50.

   (a) Write down an equation in x and y which satisfies the above condition.　　1

   The sale of the seats on this flight totalled £6000.

   (b) Write down a second equation in x and y which satisfies this condition.　　1

   (c) How many seats were sold at each price?　　4

4. A bath contains 150 litres of water.

   Water is drained from the bath at a steady rate of 30 litres per minute.

   The graph of the volume, V litres, of water in the bath against the time, t minutes, is shown below.

   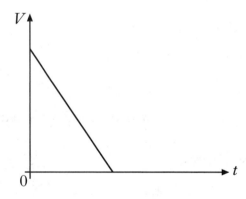

   Write down an equation connecting V and t.　　3

Marks

5. A gardener grows tomatoes in his greenhouse.

   The temperature of the greenhouse, in degrees Celsius, is recorded every day at noon for one week.

   17   22   25   16   21   16   16

   (a) For the given temperatures, calculate:

     (i) the mean;   1

   (ii) the standard deviation.   3

   Show clearly all your working.

   For best growth, the mean temperature should be $(20 \pm 5)^{\circ}$C and the standard deviation should be less than 5°C.

   (b) Are the conditions in the greenhouse likely to result in best growth?

   Explain clearly your answer.   2

   [Turn over

Marks

6. A garden trough is in the shape of a prism.

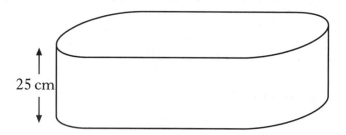

The height of the trough is 25 centimetres.

The cross-section of the trough consists of a rectangle and two semi-circles with measurements as shown.

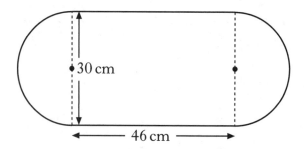

(a) Find the volume of the garden trough in cubic centimetres.

Give your answer correct to two significant figures. **4**

A new design of garden trough is planned by the manufacturer.

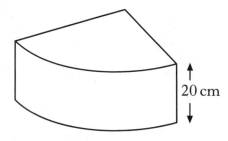

The height of the trough is 20 cm.

The uniform cross-section of this trough is a quarter of a circle.

The volume of the trough is 30 000 cm^3.

(b) Find the radius of the cross-section. **3**

Marks

7. Ali is paid a basic annual salary plus commission on his sales as shown in the table below.

Sales	Rate of commission on Sales
Less than £25 000	1·5%
£25 000 to £50 000	1·75%
More than £50 000	2·0%

His basic annual salary is **£8500**.

(a) If he achieves sales of £24 900, what will his total annual salary be?   2

(b) What would Ali's sales need to be to achieve a total annual salary of £9600?   4

8. The diagram below shows a big wheel at a fairground.

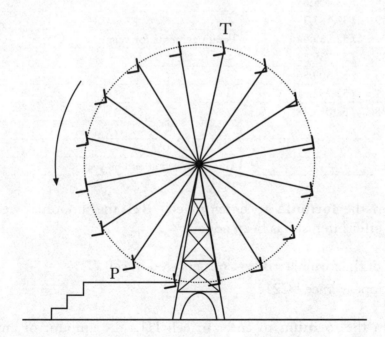

The wheel has sixteen chairs equally spaced on its circumference.

The radius of the wheel is 9 metres.

As the wheel rotates in an anticlockwise direction, find the distance a chair travels in moving from position T to position P in the diagram.   4

[Turn over

Marks

9. Irum needs a mortgage of £54 500 and wants to make payments of £500 per month.

She designs a spreadsheet to compare the costs of two mortgages.

Solid Homes Building Society calculates the interest each month (0·52% per month).

Evergreen Building Society calculates the interest each year (6·4% per annum).

	A	B	C	D	E	F	G	H
1	Solid Homes Building Society				Evergreen Building Society			
2								
3	Interest charged	0.52% per month			Interest charged	6.4% per annum		
4								
5	Amount owed		£54,500		Amount owed			£54,500
6	Monthly payment		£500		Monthly payment			£500
7								
8	Amount owed	after interest	after payment					
9								
10	January	£54,783.40	£54,283.40		Amount owed at start of year			£54,500
11	February	£54,565.67	£54,065.67					
12	March	£54,346.82	£53,846.82		Annual interest			
13	April	£54,126.82	£53,626.82					
14	May	£53,905.68	£53,405.68					
15	June	£53,683.39	£53,183.39					
16	July	£53,459.94	£52,959.94		Total payments for year			£6,000
17	August	£53,235.33	£52,735.33					
18	September	£53,009.56	£52,509.56					
19	October	£52,782.61	£52,282.61					
20	November	£52,554.48	£52,054.48					
21	December							
22								
23	Amount owed at end of year				Amount owed at end of year			

(a) Write down the **formula** to enter in cell B21 the amount owed in December after interest has been added.   1

(b) The result of the formula =B21−C6 is entered in cell C21.

What will appear in cell C21?   1

(c) Write down the **formula** to enter in cell H12 the amount of annual interest.   1

(d) Which mortgage is more expensive in the first year, and by how much?   2

Marks

10. The sketch shows a parallelogram, PQRS.

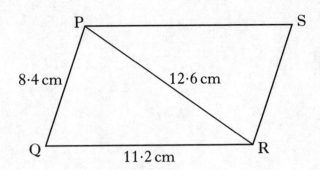

(a) Calculate the size of angle PQR.

Do not use a scale drawing.

3

(b) Calculate the area of the parallelogram.

3

11. A survey was carried out to find the average price of a washing machine.
The results are shown in the table below.

Price	Frequency	Cumulative frequency
251 – 300	8	
301 – 350	12	
351 – 400	18	
401 – 450	25	
451 – 500	19	
501 – 550	10	
551 – 600	6	
601 – 650	2	

(a) Copy and complete the table.

1

(b) Using this data, draw a cumulative frequency curve on squared paper.

3

(c) From the curve you have drawn, estimate the median price of the washing machines.

1

[END OF QUESTION PAPER]

[BLANK PAGE]

2004 | Intermediate 2

[BLANK PAGE]

X101/202

| NATIONAL
QUALIFICATIONS
2004 | FRIDAY, 21 MAY
1.00 PM – 1.45 PM | MATHEMATICS
INTERMEDIATE 2
Units 1, 2 and
Applications of Mathematics
Paper 1
(Non-calculator) |

Read carefully

1   **You may NOT use a calculator.**

2   Full credit will be given only where the solution contains appropriate working.

3   Square-ruled paper is provided.

SCOTTISH
QUALIFICATIONS
AUTHORITY

FORMULAE LIST

Sine rule: $\dfrac{a}{\sin A} = \dfrac{b}{\sin B} = \dfrac{c}{\sin C}$

Cosine rule: $a^2 = b^2 + c^2 - 2bc \cos A$ or $\cos A = \dfrac{b^2 + c^2 - a^2}{2bc}$

Area of a triangle: $\text{Area} = \frac{1}{2}ab \sin C$

Volume of a sphere: $\text{Volume} = \frac{4}{3}\pi r^3$

Volume of a cone: $\text{Volume} = \frac{1}{3}\pi r^2 h$

Volume of a cylinder: $\text{Volume} = \pi r^2 h$

Standard deviation: $s = \sqrt{\dfrac{\sum(x - \bar{x})^2}{n-1}} = \sqrt{\dfrac{\sum x^2 - (\sum x)^2 / n}{n-1}}$, where n is the sample size.

Marks

ALL questions should be attempted.

1. In a class test, the following marks were recorded.

5	9	10	4	5	5	6	10	5	8
5	7	4	9	7	5	4	6	5	7

   (a) Construct a frequency table for the above data and add a cumulative frequency column.

   2

   (b) What is the probability that a student, chosen at random from this class, obtained a mark higher than 7?

   1

2.

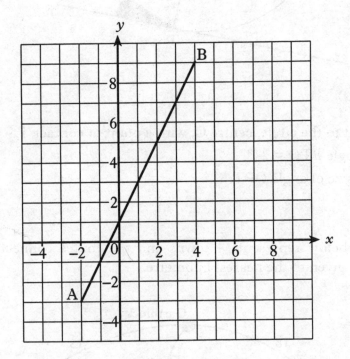

Find the equation of the straight line AB.

3

[Turn over

Marks

3.

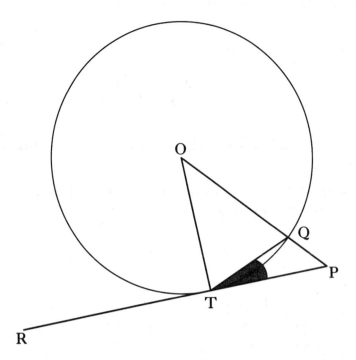

RP is a tangent to the circle, centre O, with a point of contact T.

The shaded angle PTQ = 24°.

Calculate the size of angle OPT.

3

4. The diagram below represents 4 towns and the routes connecting them, with distances given to the nearest kilometre.

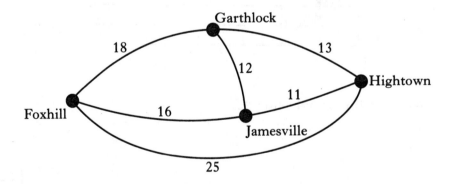

A van driver leaves Foxhill and has to make deliveries to the three other towns. He cannot go through any town more than once and does not need to return to Foxhill.

(*a*) Draw a tree diagram to show all possible delivery routes.

3

(*b*) Which is the shortest route?

2

Show clearly all working.

Marks

5. The number of chocolates in each box from a sample of 25 boxes was counted.

    The results are displayed in the dotplot below.

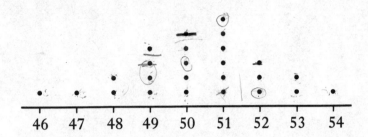

    (a) For this sample find:
        (i) the median;   1
        (ii) the lower quartile;   1
        (iii) the upper quartile.   1

    (b) Use the data from this sample to construct a boxplot.   2

    (c) In a second sample of boxes, the semi-interquartile range was 1·5.

        Make an appropriate comment about the distribution of data in the two
        samples.   2

6. The sum of the terms of a sequence of numbers is given by the formula

$$S = \frac{1}{2}n\left[2a+(n-1)d\right].$$

    (a) Calculate S when $n = 20$, $a = 5$ and $d = 3$.   2

    (b) Calculate d when $S = 664$, $a = 4$ and $n = 16$.   3

[END OF QUESTION PAPER]

[BLANK PAGE]

X101/204

NATIONAL
QUALIFICATIONS
2004

FRIDAY, 21 MAY
2.05 PM – 3.35 PM

MATHEMATICS
INTERMEDIATE 2
Units 1, 2 and
Applications of Mathematics
Paper 2

Read carefully

1 **Calculators may be used in this paper.**

2 Full credit will be given only where the solution contains appropriate working.

3 Square-ruled paper is provided.

LIB X101/204 6/7920

SCOTTISH
QUALIFICATIONS
AUTHORITY

©

FORMULAE LIST

Sine rule: $\dfrac{a}{\sin A} = \dfrac{b}{\sin B} = \dfrac{c}{\sin C}$

Cosine rule: $a^2 = b^2 + c^2 - 2bc \cos A$ or $\cos A = \dfrac{b^2 + c^2 - a^2}{2bc}$

Area of a triangle: $\text{Area} = \frac{1}{2}ab \sin C$

Volume of a sphere: $\text{Volume} = \frac{4}{3}\pi r^3$

Volume of a cone: $\text{Volume} = \frac{1}{3}\pi r^2 h$

Volume of a cylinder: $\text{Volume} = \pi r^2 h$

Standard deviation: $s = \sqrt{\dfrac{\sum (x - \bar{x})^2}{n-1}} = \sqrt{\dfrac{\sum x^2 - (\sum x)^2 / n}{n-1}}$, where n is the sample size.

ALL questions should be attempted.

Marks

1. The average Scottish house price is £77 900.

   The average price is expected to rise by 2·5% per month. What will the average Scottish house price be in 3 months?

   Give your answer correct to three significant figures.　　3

2. The heights, in millimetres, of six seedlings are given below.

   15　18　14　17　16　19

   (a) Calculate:

   　(i)　the mean;　　1

   　(ii)　the standard deviation;　　3

   of these heights.

   Show clearly all your working.

   (b) Later the same six seedlings are measured again.

   Each has grown by 4 millimetres.

   State:

   　(i)　the mean;　　1

   　(ii)　the standard deviation;　　1

   of the new heights.

   [Turn over

Marks

3. A company pays its employees travelling expenses based upon

    • miles travelled;

    • distance between home and workplace;

    • engine capacity of car;

as shown in the flowchart below.

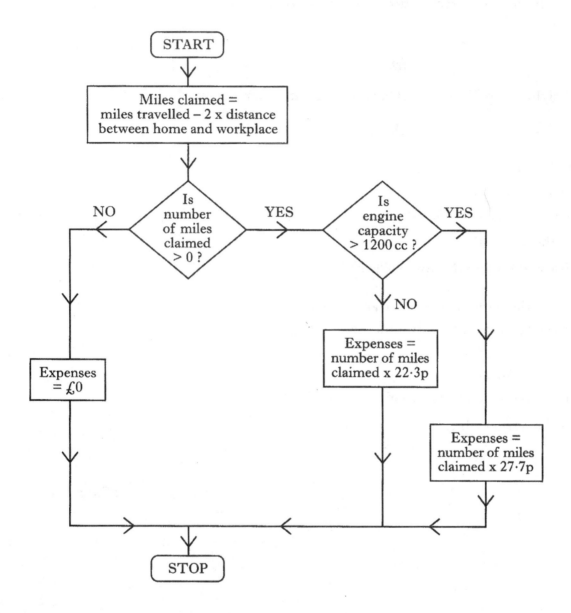

Calculate the travelling expenses paid to an employee

    • who travels 130 miles;

    • whose distance between home and workplace is 10 miles;

    • whose car has an engine capacity of 1200 cc.

3

Marks

4. The diagram shows an L-shaped metal plate.

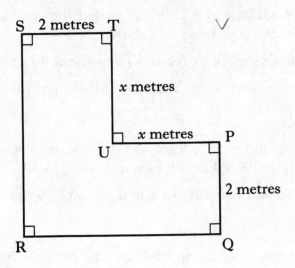

PQ = ST = 2 metres

TU = UP = x metres

(a) Show that the area, A square metres, of the metal plate is given by

$$A = 4x + 4.$$

2

(b) The area of the metal plate is 18 square metres.
Find x.

1

5.

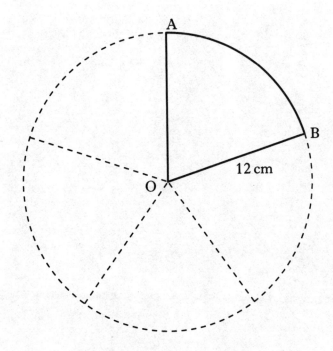

A circle with centre O and radius 12 centimetres, is cut into 5 equal sectors.

Calculate the perimeter of sector OAB.

3

Marks

6. A sports centre charges different entrance fees for adults and children.

(*a*) One evening 14 adults and 4 children visited the sports centre. The total collected in entrance fees was £55·00.

Let £x be the adult's entrance fee and £y be the child's entrance fee.

Write down an equation in x and y which represents the above condition.

1

(*b*) The following evening 13 adults and 6 children visited the sports centre. The total collected in entrance fees was £54·50.

Write down a second equation in x and y which represents the above condition.

1

(*c*) Calculate the entrance fee for an adult and the entrance fee for a child.

4

7. (*a*) Multiply out the brackets and collect like terms.

$$5x + (x - 4)(3x + 1)$$

3

(*b*) Factorise

$$3x^2 - 7x + 2.$$

2

Marks

8. The table below shows the monthly repayments to be made, with and without payment protection insurance, when money is borrowed from the Marko Loan Company.

With Payment Protection Insurance

LOAN AMOUNT	36 Months	48 Months	60 Months
	MONTHLY REPAYMENT	MONTHLY REPAYMENT	MONTHLY REPAYMENT
9·9% APR for ALL loans of £5000 – £14 999			
£5000	£186·41	£149·26	£127·31
£7500	£279.62	£223·90	£190·97
£10 000	£372·83	£298·53	£254·63
8·9% APR for ALL loans of £15 000 – £20 000			
£15 000	£549·88	£438·13	£371·86

Without Payment Protection Insurance

LOAN AMOUNT	36 Months	48 Months	60 Months
	MONTHLY REPAYMENT	MONTHLY REPAYMENT	MONTHLY REPAYMENT
9·9% APR for ALL loans of £5000 – £14 999			
£5000	£162·64	£127·54	£106·61
£7500	£243·97	£191·32	£159·92
£10 000	£325·29	£255·09	£213·22
8·9% APR for ALL loans of £15 000 – £20 000			
£15 000	£480·68	£375·40	£312·55

Fatima wants to borrow £5000 to buy a car and another £10 000 to buy a new kitchen.

She wants to make repayments over 60 months **without** payment protection insurance for **each** loan.

(a) State the monthly repayments she will make for:

   (i) the £5000 loan;

   (ii) the £10 000 loan.   **1**

Because the interest rate changes with the amount of loan, Fatima decides to check the cost of **one** loan of £15 000 over 60 months **without** payment protection insurance.

(b) How much would Fatima save over 60 months on the cost of **one** loan of £15 000 rather than two separate loans?   **3**

[Turn over

Marks

9. Perfecto Ice Cream is sold in cones and cylindrical tubs with measurements as shown below.

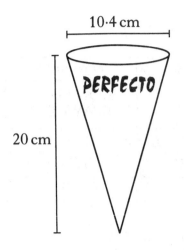
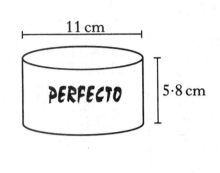

Both the cone and the tub of ice cream cost the same.

Which container of ice cream is better value for money?

Give a reason for your answer.

5

10. A nurse earns £18 650 per year and has tax allowances totalling £4670.

    (a) Calculate the nurse's taxable income.

1

    (b) The rates of tax applicable are as follows.

TAXABLE INCOME (£)	RATE
On the first £1920	10%
On the next £27 980	22%
On any income over £29 900	40%

    Calculate the amount of tax payable by the nurse.

3

Marks

11. A garden, in the shape of a quadrilateral, is represented in the diagram below.

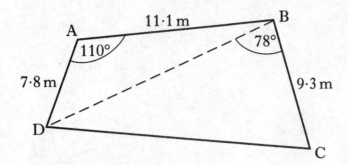

Calculate:

(a) the length of the diagonal BD;

   Do not use a scale drawing 3

(b) the area of the garden. 4

12. A company keeps a record of how many days each employee is absent over a two-year period.

The results are shown in the frequency table below.

Number of days absent	Frequency
0 – 4	14
5 – 9	17
10 – 14	8
15 – 19	4
20 – 24	2

Calculate the mean number of days an employee is absent. 5

[END OF QUESTION PAPER]

[BLANK PAGE]

2005 | Intermediate 2

[BLANK PAGE]

X101/202

NATIONAL
QUALIFICATIONS
2005

FRIDAY, 20 MAY
1.00 PM – 1.45 PM

MATHEMATICS
INTERMEDIATE 2
Units 1, 2 and
Applications of Mathematics
Paper 1
(Non-calculator)

Read carefully

1   **You may NOT use a calculator.**

2   Full credit will be given only where the solution contains appropriate working.

3   Square-ruled paper is provided.

SCOTTISH
QUALIFICATIONS
AUTHORITY

FORMULAE LIST

Sine rule: $\dfrac{a}{\sin A} = \dfrac{b}{\sin B} = \dfrac{c}{\sin C}$

Cosine rule: $a^2 = b^2 + c^2 - 2bc \cos A$ or $\cos A = \dfrac{b^2 + c^2 - a^2}{2bc}$

Area of a triangle: $\text{Area} = \tfrac{1}{2}ab \sin C$

Volume of a sphere: $\text{Volume} = \tfrac{4}{3}\pi r^3$

Volume of a cone: $\text{Volume} = \tfrac{1}{3}\pi r^2 h$

Volume of a cylinder: $\text{Volume} = \pi r^2 h$

Standard deviation: $s = \sqrt{\dfrac{\sum (x - \bar{x})^2}{n-1}} = \sqrt{\dfrac{\sum x^2 - (\sum x)^2 / n}{n-1}}$, where n is the sample size.

Marks

ALL questions should be attempted.

1. The stem and leaf diagram below shows the heights of a group of children.

$$
\begin{array}{c|cccccc}
12 & 1 & 2 & 4 & 5 & 9 \\
13 & 0 & 0 & 1 & 5 & 7 & 8 \\
14 & 0 & 2 & 8 & 9 \\
15 & 1 & 1 & 2
\end{array}
$$

    n = 18   12 | 1 represents 121 centimetres

    What is the probability that a child chosen at random from this group has a
    height less than 130 centimetres?   1

2.

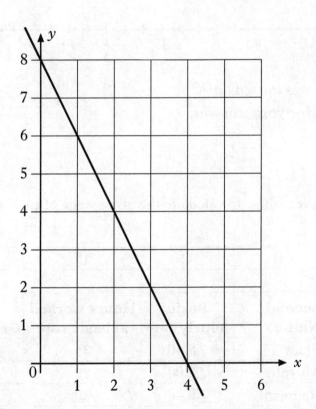

    (a) Find the equation of the straight line shown in the diagram.   3

    (b) Find the coordinates of the point where the line $y = 2x$ meets this line. 2

3. (a) Multiply out the brackets and collect like terms.

$$(4x + 2)(x - 5) + 3x$$

                                                                                  3

    (b) Factorise

$$2p^2 - 5p - 12.$$

                                                                                  2

Marks

4. For a group of freezers in a shop, the volume, in litres, of each one is listed below.

78   81   91   75   85   83   84   78

(a) For the given data, calculate:

  (i) the median; 1

  (ii) the lower quartile; 1

  (iii) the upper quartile. 1

One of the numbers from the above list was accidentally missed out. A boxplot was then drawn and is shown below.

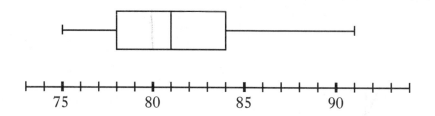

(b) Which number was missed out?

Give a reason for your answer. 2

5. A manager uses a spreadsheet to calculate the gross wage of each worker.

	A	B	C	D	E
1					
2	**First Name**	**Second Name**	**Basic hourly rate**	**Hours worked at basic rate**	**Gross wage**
3	Joseph	Shaw	£8.40	36	£302.40
4	Mary	Murphy	£8.00	20	
5	Irum	Rahman	£6.40	30	
6	Stephen	Sheilds	£6.00	24	
7	Miriam	Philips	£4.50	16	
8					
9					
10		**Average gross wage per worker =**			

(a) The result of the formula =C5*D5 is entered in cell E5.

What will appear in cell E5? 1

(b) Write down the **formula** to enter in cell E10 the average gross wage per worker. 1

Marks

6. Given that

$$\tan 45° = 1,$$

what is the value of $\tan 135°$?

1

7. A network is **traversable** if it can be drawn by going over every line once and only once without lifting your pencil.

The network shown opposite can be traversed by the route

$S→P→Q→S→R→Q→T$

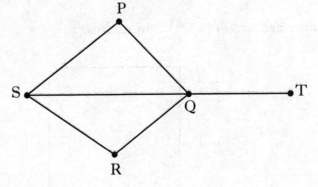

Is the network below traversable?

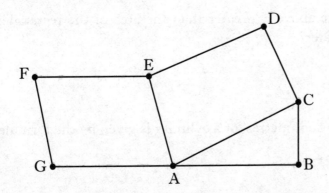

Explain your answer.

2

[Turn over for Questions 8 and 9 on *Page six*

Marks

8. A rectangle has length $(x + 2)$ centimetres and breadth x centimetres.

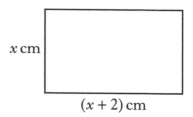

x cm

$(x + 2)$ cm

(a) Write down an expression for the area of the rectangle. **1**

A square has length $(x + 1)$ centimetres.

$(x + 1)$ cm

(b) The area of the square above is greater than the area of the rectangle. By how much is it greater? **2**

9. The surface area, S square centimetres, of a cylinder is given by the formula

$$S = 2\pi r^2 + 2\pi r h$$

where r centimetres is the radius of the base
and h centimetres is the height.

Take $\pi = 3\cdot14$.

(a) Calculate S when $r = 3$ and $h = 7$. **3**

(b) Calculate h when $S = 471$ and $r = 5$. **3**

[END OF QUESTION PAPER]

X101/204

NATIONAL
QUALIFICATIONS
2005

FRIDAY, 20 MAY
2.05 PM – 3.35 PM

MATHEMATICS
INTERMEDIATE 2
Units 1, 2 and
Applications of Mathematics
Paper 2

Read carefully

1   **Calculators may be used in this paper.**

2   Full credit will be given only where the solution contains appropriate working.

3   Square-ruled paper is provided.

SCOTTISH
QUALIFICATIONS
AUTHORITY

FORMULAE LIST

Sine rule: $\dfrac{a}{\sin A} = \dfrac{b}{\sin B} = \dfrac{c}{\sin C}$

Cosine rule: $a^2 = b^2 + c^2 - 2bc \cos A$ or $\cos A = \dfrac{b^2 + c^2 - a^2}{2bc}$

Area of a triangle: $\text{Area} = \frac{1}{2}ab \sin C$

Volume of a sphere: $\text{Volume} = \frac{4}{3}\pi r^3$

Volume of a cone: $\text{Volume} = \frac{1}{3}\pi r^2 h$

Volume of a cylinder: $\text{Volume} = \pi r^2 h$

Standard deviation: $s = \sqrt{\dfrac{\sum (x - \bar{x})^2}{n-1}} = \sqrt{\dfrac{\sum x^2 - (\sum x)^2 / n}{n-1}}$, where n is the sample size.

ALL questions should be attempted.

Marks

1. In the evening, the temperature in a greenhouse drops by 4% per hour.

    At 8 pm the temperature is $28\,°$ Celsius.

    What will the temperature be at 11 pm?

    3

2. In a bakery, a sample of six fruit loaves is selected and the weights, in grams, are recorded.

    $$395 \quad 400 \quad 408 \quad 390 \quad 405 \quad 402$$

    For the above data the mean is found to be 400 grams.

    (a) Calculate the standard deviation.

    Show clearly all your working.

    3

    (b) New methods are introduced to ensure more consistent weights.

    Another sample is then taken and the mean and standard deviation found to be 400 grams and 5·8 grams respectively.

    Are the new methods successful?

    Give a reason for your answer.

    1

3. Sandy works in a call centre for a company selling conservatories.

    Her pay is calculated as follows:

    - for each client who agrees to a home visit from a salesman she is paid £10
    - for each one of her clients who places an order for a conservatory she is paid 0·5% commission on the sale.

    One week 20 of Sandy's clients agree to a home visit.
    One of them orders a conservatory worth £12 000.

    Calculate Sandy's pay for the week.

    2

4. A straight line has equation $3y = 12 - 4x$.

    Find the coordinates of the point where it crosses the x-axis.

    2

[Turn over

Marks

5. A jeweller uses two different arrangements of beads and pearls.

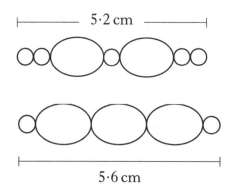

5·2 cm

5·6 cm

The first arrangement consists of 2 beads and 5 pearls and has an overall length of 5·2 centimetres.

The second arrangement consists of 3 beads and 2 pearls and has an overall length of 5·6 centimetres.

Find the length of **one** bead and the length of **one** pearl.

6

6. The table shown below is used to calculate loan repayments.

Monthly repayments on a loan of £1000

APR	12 months	24 months	36 months	48 months
12%	£88·56	£46·79	£32·92	£26·03
14%	£89·40	£47·62	£33·78	£26·91
16%	£90·23	£48·46	£34·63	£27·80
18%	£91·05	£49·28	£35·49	£28·68
20%	£91·86	£50·10	£36·34	£29·57

Jack Smith borrows £3500 over 36 months at an annual percentage rate (APR) of 14%.

Use the table to calculate the total cost of the loan.

4

Marks

7. The diagram below shows a sector of a circle, centre C.

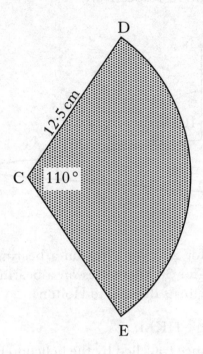

The radius of the circle is 12·5 centimetres and angle DCE is 110°.

Calculate the area of the sector CDE.   3

[Turn over

Marks

8. In the diagram below three towns, Holton, Kilter and Malbrigg are represented by the points H, K and M respectively.

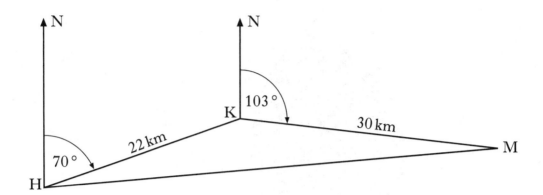

A helicopter flies from Holton for 22 kilometres on a bearing of 070° to Kilter. It then flies from Kilter for 30 kilometres on a bearing of 103° to Malbrigg. The helicopter then returns directly to Holton.

(*a*) (i) Calculate the size of angle HKM. **1**

   (ii) Calculate the total distance travelled by the helicopter. **3**

   Do not use a scale drawing.

(*b*) A climber is reported missing somewhere in the triangle represented by HKM in the diagram.

   Calculate the area of this triangle. **2**

9. A pharmaceutical company makes vitamin pills in the shape of spheres of radius 0·5 centimetres.

(*a*) Calculate the volume of **one** pill.

   Give your answer correct to two significant figures. **3**

The company decides to change the shape of each pill to a cylinder.

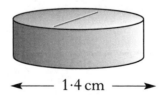

1·4 cm

(*b*) The new pill has the **same** volume as the original and its diameter is 1·4 centimetres.

   Calculate the height of the new pill. **3**

Marks

10. Below is a copy of Louise Green's credit card statement.

Visa **statement**	**Suremoney Financial Services**
Name: Louise Green	

Date: 20 May 2005

Account No: 2351 1137   Credit limit: £850

Interest rate: 1·5% per month

Please post your payment to arrive by 10 June 2005

29 April 2005	Balance brought forward	120·00
7 May 2005	Payment—*Thank you*	−50·00
		70·00
	Interest	1·05
10 May 2005	Dynamic Dancewear	42·75
14 May 2005	Taps and Tutus	13·81
15 May 2005	Hall Rentals	256·00
	Balance owed	383·61

Minimum payment: 3% of balance owed

Note: *Interest is charged each month on outstanding balance after payment is deducted.*

(a) Louise makes the minimum payment. How much does she pay?   **2**

(b) If Louise does not add any items to her credit card during the next month, calculate the "balance owed" on her next statement.   **3**

[Turn over

Marks

11. Points A, B and C lie on the circumference of a circle, centre O.

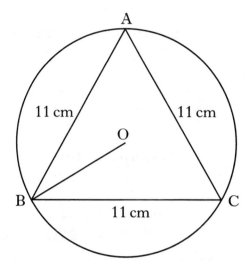

Triangle ABC is equilateral with sides of length 11 centimetres as shown in the diagram.

(*a*) Write down the size of angle OBC. **1**

(*b*) Calculate the length of the radius OB. **3**

Marks

12. A sample of 40 light bulbs was chosen at random and tested to see how long each bulb lasted.

The results are shown below.

Life of bulb (*t* hours)	Frequency
$1200 \le t < 1300$	3
$1300 \le t < 1400$	4
$1400 \le t < 1500$	3
$1500 \le t < 1600$	4
$1600 \le t < 1700$	5
$1700 \le t < 1800$	6
$1800 \le t < 1900$	9
$1900 \le t < 2000$	6

(a) Construct a cumulative frequency column for the above data. 1

(b) Using squared paper, draw a cumulative frequency diagram for this data. 3

(c) From your diagram, estimate the median number of hours a light bulb lasts. 1

[END OF QUESTION PAPER]

[BLANK PAGE]

[BLANK PAGE]

2006 | Intermediate 2

[BLANK PAGE]

X101/202

NATIONAL
QUALIFICATIONS
2006

FRIDAY, 19 MAY
1.00 PM – 1.45 PM

MATHEMATICS
INTERMEDIATE 2
Units 1, 2 and
Applications of Mathematics
Paper 1
(Non-calculator)

Read carefully

1   **You may <u>NOT</u> use a calculator.**

2   Full credit will be given only where the solution contains appropriate working.

3   Square-ruled paper is provided.

SCOTTISH
QUALIFICATIONS
AUTHORITY

FORMULAE LIST

Sine rule: $\dfrac{a}{\sin A} = \dfrac{b}{\sin B} = \dfrac{c}{\sin C}$

Cosine rule: $a^2 = b^2 + c^2 - 2bc \cos A$ or $\cos A = \dfrac{b^2 + c^2 - a^2}{2bc}$

Area of a triangle: $\text{Area} = \frac{1}{2}ab \sin C$

Volume of a sphere: $\text{Volume} = \frac{4}{3}\pi r^3$

Volume of a cone: $\text{Volume} = \frac{1}{3}\pi r^2 h$

Volume of a cylinder: $\text{Volume} = \pi r^2 h$

Standard deviation: $s = \sqrt{\dfrac{\sum(x - \bar{x})^2}{n-1}} = \sqrt{\dfrac{\sum x^2 - (\sum x)^2 / n}{n-1}}$, where n is the sample size.

Marks

ALL questions should be attempted.

1. The temperature, in degrees Celsius, at mid-day in a seaside town and the sales, in pounds, of umbrellas are shown in the scattergraph below.

   A line of best fit has been drawn.

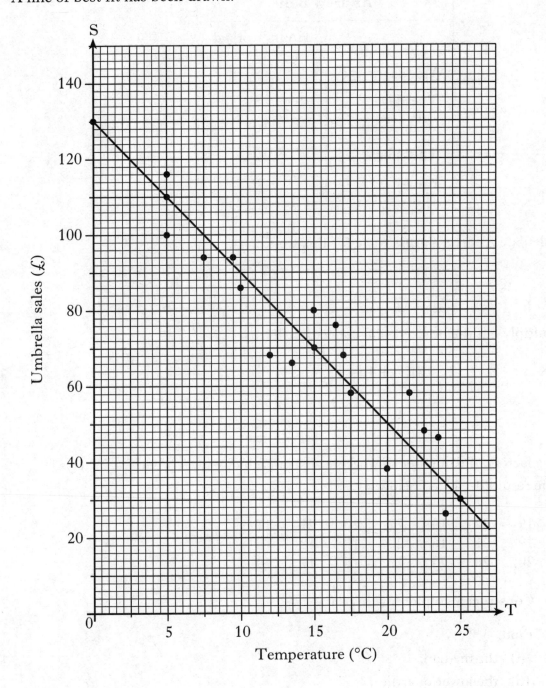

(a) Find the equation of the line of best fit.   **3**

(b) **Use your answer to part (a)** to predict the sales for a day when the temperature is 30 degrees Celsius.   **1**

[Turn over

Marks

2. Andrew Bell works in a factory. He works a basic 8 hour day at a rate of £6·40 per hour. Additional hours worked are paid at time and a half.

   Andrew's timesheet for one week's work is shown below.

Andrew Bell	
	Hours worked
Monday	8
Tuesday	8
Wednesday	10
Thursday	10
Friday	8

   Calculate Andrew's gross wage for this week.

   3

3. Multiply out the brackets and collect like terms.

   $$(2y - 3)(y^2 + 4y - 1)$$

   3

4. In a factory, the number of workers absent each day is recorded for 21 days. The results are listed below.

19	22	19	22	20	21	17
19	21	16	20	19	18	18
20	20	23	19	18	17	19

   (a) Construct a dotplot for this data.

   2

   (b) Find:

   (i) the median;

   1

   (ii) the lower quartile;

   1

   (iii) the upper quartile.

   1

   (c) What is the probability that, on a day chosen at random from this sample, more than 18 workers were absent?

   1

Marks

5. Anthony is going to cook chicken escalope in breadcrumbs with spaghetti in a tomato and basil sauce.

He has four rings on his cooker, allowing the different dishes to be cooked at the same time.

The network below shows how this can be done.

Times are given in minutes.

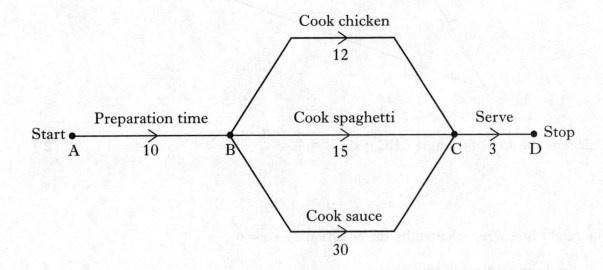

By considering the **critical path** from start to finish of this network, find the minimum time needed to complete the job.　　　　1

6. The formula below converts temperature from Celsius (C) to Fahrenheit (F).

$$F = 32 + \frac{9}{5}C$$

Use this formula to convert 25 °Celsius to Fahrenheit.　　　　2

[Turn over

Marks

7.

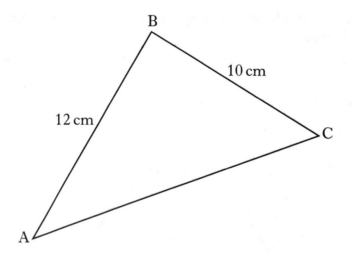

Calculate the area of triangle ABC if sin B = $\frac{2}{3}$.

2

8. A straight line is represented by the equation $2y + x = 6$.

(a) Find the gradient of this line.

2

(b) This line crosses the *y*-axis at $(0, c)$.
Find the value of *c*.

1

9. Write the following in order of size, **starting with the smallest**.

sin 0°   sin 30°   sin 200°

Give a reason for your answer.

2

10. A group of 1000 pupils sit a test marked out of 12.

The cumulative frequency curve derived from their marks is shown below.

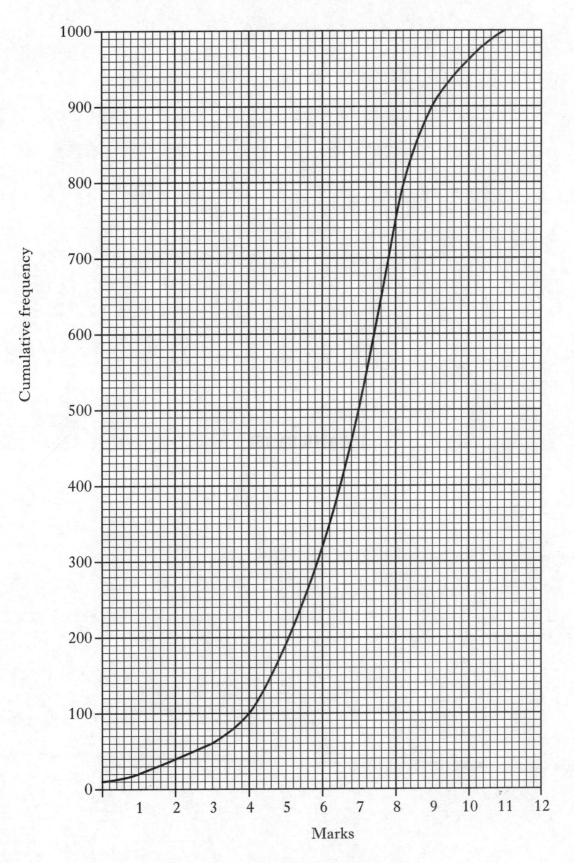

Use this information to draw a boxplot of the marks.

4

[END OF QUESTION PAPER]

[BLANK PAGE]

X101/204

NATIONAL
QUALIFICATIONS
2006

FRIDAY, 19 MAY
2.05 PM – 3.35 PM

MATHEMATICS
INTERMEDIATE 2
Units 1, 2 and
Applications of Mathematics
Paper 2

Read carefully

1 **Calculators may be used in this paper.**

2 Full credit will be given only where the solution contains appropriate working.

3 Square-ruled paper is provided.

SCOTTISH
QUALIFICATIONS
AUTHORITY

FORMULAE LIST

Sine rule: $\dfrac{a}{\sin A} = \dfrac{b}{\sin B} = \dfrac{c}{\sin C}$

Cosine rule: $a^2 = b^2 + c^2 - 2bc \cos A$ or $\cos A = \dfrac{b^2 + c^2 - a^2}{2bc}$

Area of a triangle: Area $= \frac{1}{2}ab \sin C$

Volume of a sphere: Volume $= \frac{4}{3}\pi r^3$

Volume of a cone: Volume $= \frac{1}{3}\pi r^2 h$

Volume of a cylinder: Volume $= \pi r^2 h$

Standard deviation: $s = \sqrt{\dfrac{\sum(x - \bar{x})^2}{n-1}} = \sqrt{\dfrac{\sum x^2 - (\sum x)^2 / n}{n-1}}$, where n is the sample size.

ALL questions should be attempted.

Marks

1. The value of a boat decreased from £35 000 to £32 200 in one year.

   (*a*) What was the percentage decrease? 1

   (*b*) If the value of the boat continued to fall at this rate, what would its value be after a **further** 3 years?

   Give your answer to the nearest hundred pounds. 3

2. Solve algebraically the system of equations

   $$4x + 2y = 13$$

   $$5x + 3y = 17.$$ 3

3. Factorise

   $$4p^2 - 49.$$ 2

[Turn over

Marks

4. Sajid has borrowed £200 with interest accumulating at 1·5% each month.
   The spreadsheet shows the amount owed at the beginning of each month.

	A	B
1	Month	
2	January	£200.00
3	February	£203.00
4	March	£206.05
5	April	£209.14
6	May	£212.27
7	June	£215.46
8	July	£218.69
9	August	£221.97
10	September	£225.30
11	October	£228.68
12	November	£232.11
13	December	£235.59
14	January	
15		
16	APR	

(a) Write down the **formula** to enter in cell B14 the amount owed at the beginning of January. 1

(b) The Annual Percentage Rate (APR) for a monthly interest rate of 1·5% can be calculated using the formula = (B14 − B2)/B2*100.
    Calculate the APR. 3

Marks

5. A new central heating system is installed in a house.

Sample temperatures, in degrees Celsius, are recorded below.

$$19 \quad 21 \quad 23 \quad 21 \quad 19 \quad 20$$

(a) For this sample data, calculate:

(i) the mean;   1

(ii) the standard deviation.   3

Show clearly all your working.

The target temperature for this house is 20 °Celsius. The system is judged to be operating effectively if the mean temperature is within 0·6 °Celsius of the target temperature **and** the standard deviation is less than 2 °Celsius.

(b) Is the system operating effectively?

Give reasons for your answer.   2

6. The diagram shows the base of a compact disc stand which has the shape of part of a circle.

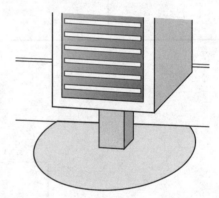

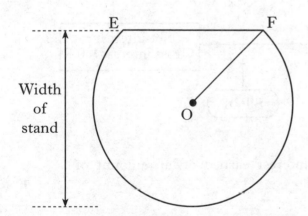

- The centre of the circle is O.
- EF is a chord of the circle.
- EF is 18 centimetres.
- The radius, OF, of the circle is 15 centimetres.

Find the width of the stand.   4

[Turn over

Marks

7. The flowchart below shows how to calculate the **net** interest when a certain sum of money is invested for 1 year.

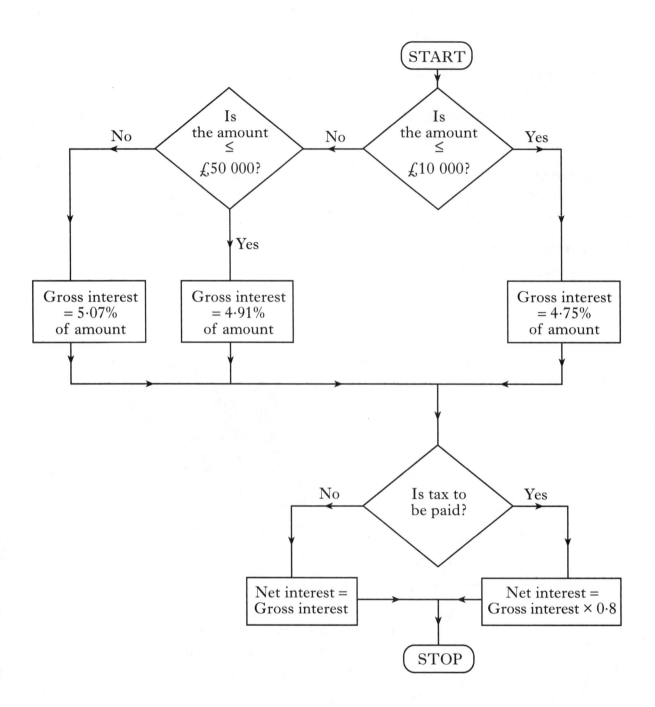

Use the flowchart to calculate the net interest earned on an amount of £58 500 invested by a tax payer for 1 year.

4

Marks

8. A child's toy is in the shape of a hemisphere with a cone on top, as shown in the diagram.

   The toy is 10 centimetres wide and 16 centimetres high.

   Calculate the volume of the toy.

   Give your answer correct to 2 significant figures.

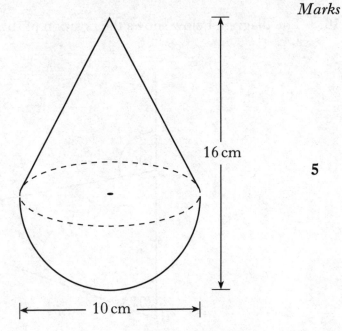

5

9. Jock McFadzean is a plumber. He earns £38 750 in one year. He has tax allowances of £4745.

   The rates of tax applicable for the year are given in the table below.

Taxable income (£)	Rate
On the first £1960	10%
On the next £28 540	22%
On any income over £30 500	40%

   How much was Jock's **weekly** tax bill during the year?

5

[Turn over

Marks

10. The diagram below shows the position of three campsites A, B and C.

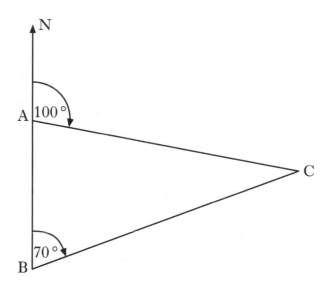

Alan sets off from campsite A on a bearing of 100° at an average speed of 5·6 kilometres per hour.

At the same time Bob sets off from campsite B on a bearing of 070°.

After 3 hours they both arrive at campsite C.

Who has the faster average speed and by how much?

5

Marks

11. The tables below show the monthly repayments to be made, with and without payment protection, when £1000 is borrowed from the Bettervalue Loan Firm.

Without Payment Protection				
APR on £1000	12 months	24 months	36 months	48 months
10%	£88·82	£47·05	£33·17	£26·26
12%	£89·66	£47·89	£34·02	£27·13
14%	£90·50	£48·72	£34·88	£28·01
16%	£91·33	£49·56	£35·73	£28·90

With Payment Protection				
APR on £1000	12 months	24 months	36 months	48 months
10%	£94·96	£51·64	£37·33	£30·03
12%	£95·86	£52·57	£38·30	£31·04
14%	£96·76	£53·49	£39·27	£32·05
16%	£97·64	£54·40	£40·24	£33·07

Jean needs a loan. She can afford to pay £220 per month, and wants the biggest loan she can get over 36 months, without payment protection.

How much can she borrow from Bettervalue Loan Firm at 14% APR?

Give your answer to the nearest £100.

3

[Turn over for Question 12 on *Page ten*

Marks

12. The diagram shows the penalty area in a football pitch.

All measurements are given in yards.

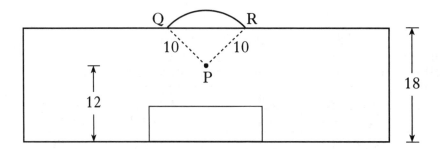

The penalty spot is marked at point P.

QR is an arc of a circle, centre P, radius 10 yards.

The width of the penalty area is 18 yards and the distance of the penalty spot from the goal line is 12 yards, as shown.

(*a*) Calculate the size of angle QPR. **3**

(*b*) Calculate the length of arc QR. **2**

[END OF QUESTION PAPER]

[BLANK PAGE]

[BLANK PAGE]